advance music | play-along

Jim Snidero

Jazz Conception
Alto & Baritone Saxophone

21 solo etudes
for jazz phrasing,
interpretation
and improvisation
played by
Jim Snidero

includes online audio material

ADV 14720
ISMN 979-0-2063-0398-2
ISBN 978-3-95481-033-8

advance music

www.advancemusic.com | © 1996/2015/2021 advance music GmbH, Mainz | Printed in Germany

Cover Image: 10eg

Cover Design: Elke Dörr

Music engraving: Walter Gruber

Production: Hans Gruber

Musicians on the recording:
Jim Snidero – Alto Saxophone
Mike LeDonne – Piano
Dennis Irwin – Bass
Kenny Washington – Drums

Recorded at Steve Davis Studios.
Engineer – Steve Davis
Producer – Jim Snidero

Executive producer – Hans Gruber

Special thanks to Hans Gruber for his encouragement and support,
and to Conrad, Walt, Joe and Mike, whose input was invaluable.

TABLE OF CONTENTS

Please visit **www.schott-music.com/online-material** to download all audio files for free using the following voucher code: **ATBs4jmx**

Auf der Website **www.schott-music.com/online-material** können alle Audio-Dateien mit dem folgenden Gutscheincode kostenlos heruntergeladen werden: **ATBs4jmx**

Sur le site **www.schott-music.com/online-material** vous pouvez accéder et télécharger gratuitement toutes les pistes audio en utilisant le code suivant: **ATBs4jmx**

INTRODUCTION

Here are both a few notes on the phrasing markings and some suggestions on how to practice the etudes. Although articulation and phrasing markings are provided, the best way to understand these very important details is to listen to and copy the soloist on the recording.

ON PHRASING AND ARTICULATION MARKINGS

A *marcato* (∧) marking on a quarter note means separated but still with some weight.

Quarter notes and eighth notes that are on the "and" of the beat with a *marcato* (∧) are basically the same sound.

In general, eighth-note lines are *legato*.

Most bends are subtle shadings done with a slight movement of the jaw.

The ✕ mark indicates a muting of the reed, done with the tongue.

SOME IMPORTANT POINTS ON PRACTICING THE ETUDES

Practice them slowly at first, with a metronome. If you feel tense or confused, you're going too fast.

Practice along with the soloist and rhythm section. Try to copy the articulation, phrasing, sound and time feel.

Practice playing along to the rhythm section only, using the corresponding play-along track.

Definitely try to memorize the etudes. This will really help internalize everything.

Take as many ideas as you can from the etudes and use them in your improvised solos.

When playing along with the recording, alternate between playing the etude and improvising (example: play the first chorus, improvise on the second chorus, play the tag).

Even though there are many phrasings marked, it's impossible to indicate what's totally going on in a musical sense. This is something you have to hear and absorb. The markings are only a reference. You may eventually want to phrase some things differently, which is fine as long as what you do sounds good. But first try them the way they are marked.

Try transposing some or all of the etudes (Example: F to G♭). This will increase your understanding of them, and improve your technique.

Practice the etudes with other musicians who play different instruments. This will help develop your ensemble playing.

This book is not meant as a replacement for transcribing and listening. It is meant as an introduction and supplement, a kind of conceptual bridge to the masters. It is really a tribute to them. I hope that you find it both enjoyable and useful.

EINFÜHRUNG

Ein paar Bemerkungen zu den Artikulationszeichen sowie Anregungen zum Üben dieser Etüden. Die Etüden enthalten zwar Artikulations- und Phrasierungszeichen, der beste Weg diese wichtigen Details zu verstehen, ist jedoch das Anhören und Kopieren des Solisten auf der Aufnahme.

ÜBER PHRASIERUNGS- UND ARTIKULATIONSZEICHEN

Ein *marcato* (∧) Zeichen über einer Viertelnote bedeutet, dass diese Note abgesetzt und mit etwas mehr Gewicht gespielt wird.

Viertel- und Achtelnoten mit einem stehenden Marcatozeichen, die auf die "und" fallen, klingen praktisch gleich.

Melodielinien, die aus Achtelnoten bestehen, werden grundsätzlich *legato* gespielt.

Die meisten gezogenen (bend) Noten werden durch eine leichte Bewegung des Kiefers manipuliert.

Ein ✕ bedeutet, dass dieser Ton mit der Zunge am Blatt gedämpft wird.

EINIGE WICHTIGE PUNKTE ZUM ÜBEN DIESER ETÜDEN

Zuerst langsam mit einem Metronom üben. Wenn Sie zu angespannt oder konfus sind, dann ist wahrscheinlich das Tempo zu schnell.

Üben Sie mit dem Solisten und der Rhythmusgruppe. Versuchen Sie, Artikulation, Phrasierung, Klang und *time feel* zu kopieren.

Üben Sie auch, nur mit der Rhythmusgruppe zu spielen, indem Sie den entsprechenden Play-Along Track auswählen.

Versuchen Sie unbedingt die Etüden auswendig zu lernen. Das wird Ihnen helfen das Ganze zu verinnerlichen.

Verwenden Sie möglichst viele Ideen von den Etüden in Ihren eigenen improvisierten Soli.

Wechseln Sie zwischen Etüde und Improvisation hin und her (Beispiel: Spielen Sie den ersten Chorus wie notiert, improvisieren Sie im zweiten Chorus und spielen Sie den notierten *Tag* [Anhang]).

Sehr viele Phrasierungszeichen sind notiert, trotzdem ist es unmöglich alle musikalischen Nuancen des Solisten ganz exakt aufzuschreiben. Das müssen Sie heraushören und absorbieren. Die Phrasierungszeichen sind nur eine Referenz. Sie wollen vielleicht einige Stellen anders phrasieren, das ist in Ordnung, solange es gut klingt. Versuchen Sie aber zuerst die Etüden so zu spielen, wie sie notiert sind.

Transponieren Sie einige oder alle Etüden in andere Tonarten (Beispiel: F to G♭). Dadurch werden Sie die Etüden noch besser kennenlernen, und es wird zudem Ihre Technik verbessern.

Üben Sie die Etüden mit anderen Instrumentalisten, es wird Ihr Satzspiel verbessern.

Dieses Heft ist nicht als Ersatz für das Transkribieren und Hören gedacht. Es ist vielmehr eine Einführung und eine Ergänzung, eine Art konzeptioneller Brücke zu den grossen Musikern des Jazz. Ich hoffe, dass Sie Spass damit haben, und dass sie Ihnen auch etwas bringen.

INTRODUCTION

Quelques remarques concernant les signes d'articulation, ainsi que des suggestions pour le travail de ces études. Ces études comportent de fait de nombreuses indications d'articulation et de phrasé, et la meilleure manière d'appréhender ces importants détails consiste certainement à écouter et à copier ce que fait le soliste sur les enregistrements. Après avoir ainsi formé votre oreille et vous être rendu capable d'entendre ces détails, essayez de percevoir de vous-même les articulations et les phrasés du soliste dans les autres morceaux.

LES SIGNES D'ARTICULATION ET DE PHRASÉ

Un signe de marcato (∧) au-dessus d'une noire signifie que la note doit être détachée et jouée avec un peu plus de poids.

Les noires et les croches marquées d'un signe de marcato situé sur un „et" (sur la partie faible du temps) sonnent pratiquement de manière égale.

Les lignes mélodiques de croches sont par principe jouées *legato*. La plupart des notes tirées (*bend*) peuvent être manipulées par un petit mouvement de la mâchoire. Le signe ✖ indique un silence du cuivre fait avec la langue.

QUELQUES POINTS IMPORTANTS DANS LE TRAVAIL DE CES ÉTUDES

Travaillez d'abord lentement au métronome. Si vous vous sentez tendu ou troublé, c'est sans doute que le tempo est trop rapide.

Travaillez avec le soliste et la rythmique. Essayez de reproduire l'articulation, le phrasé, la sonorité et le time feel.

Travaillez avec la rythmique seule, en selectionnant la piste correspondante.

Essayez absolument d'apprendre ces études par cœur. Cela vous aidera à intérioriser le tout.

Ayez autant que possible recours aux idées des études dans vos improvisations solistiques personnelles.

Passez de l'Étude à l'improvisation, et vice-versa (par exemple, jouez le premier chorus comme il est noté, improvisez le deuxième chorus, et jouez le tag (annexe) tel qu'il est noté).

Il y a beaucoup de signes de phrasé notés, mais il est pourtant impossible d'écrire avec exactitude toutes les nuances musicales demandées au soliste. C'est cela que vous devez percevoir et absorber. Les indications de phrasé ne sont que des références. Si vous voulez phraser autrement à tel ou tel endroit, c'est sans problème, tant que ça sonne bien. Mais essayez d'abord de jouer les études telles qu'elles ont été enregistrées.

Transposez-en certaines (ou toutes) dans d'autres tonalités (par exemple, de Fa à Sol). Ceci vous amènera à les connaître encore mieux, et contribuera à améliorer votre technique.

Travaillez ces études avec d'autres instrumentistes, ceci améliorera votre style.

Ce recueil n'est pas un succédané d'exercice de transcription et d'audition. C'est beaucoup plus une introduction et un complément, une sorte de pont conceptuel vers les grands musiciens de jazz. J'espère que vous y prendrez plaisir, et qu'elles vous apporteront aussi quelque chose.

THE BAND

Jim Snidero

Mike LeDonne

Kenny Washington

Dennis Irwin

Groove Blues

Jim Snidero

©1996 advance music GmbH, mainz | ADV 14720

Amen

Jim Snidero

* = muting of the reed, done with the tongue.
* = dieser Ton wird mit der Zunge am Blatt abgedämpft.
* = silence du cuivre, effectué avec la langue

A Doll

Jim Snidero

Total Blues

Jim Snidero

Grease

Jim Snidero

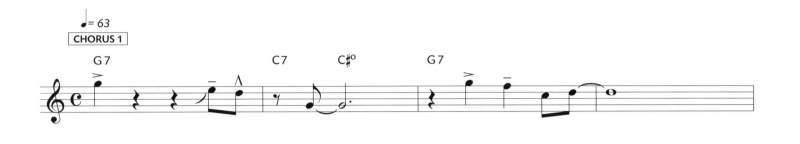

Rose

Jim Snidero

Joe's Thing

Jim Snidero

Proxy

Jim Snidero

Track 11/32

Father Song

Jim Snidero

- 22 -

IND Line

Jim Snidero

Miles

Jim Snidero

Blue Minor

Jim Snidero

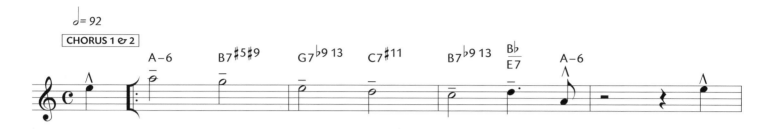

Autumn

Jim Snidero

Friends

Jim Snidero

Great Love

Jim Snidero

Two Plus Two

Jim Snidero

- 36 -

Lunar

Jim Snidero

Tunisia

Jim Snidero

Bird Blues

Jim Snidero

Delayed Resolution
résolution retardée

Somewhere

Jim Snidero

Passage

Jim Snidero

advance music GmbH, Mainz | ADV 14720

APPENDIX

JAZZ STYLE

Simply put, *style* is the thing that brings music alive. Over the many years I worked with Frank Sinatra, a master of style, I quickly realized that what you do to the notes is just as important as the actual pitches themselves. Style adds a human quality that makes music much more interesting and satisfying, and is critical in sounding both convincing and authentic in jazz.

The essential elements of jazz style are *sound, time feel, articulation, phrasing, vibrato, and dynamics,* combined with a sense of *musicality.* The only way to develop these elements is to listen intensely to great players and practice re-creating their style. The provided recording will give you great examples of all these elements.

SOUND: When asked how he could get his sound on any saxophone, the great saxophonist Sonny Stitt told Ken Peplowski that "it's all in your head." What he meant is that the concept of the sound is something that you hear internally, after developing an idea of how you want to sound by studying great players. Try hearing the sound of the soloist in your head and re-create it when practicing the etudes. Listen especially for color, center and intensity.

TIME FEEL: No matter what type of music is being played, the best musicians make what they play feel good. This usually means keeping the music at the same time both relaxed and intense (as opposed to lazy feeling), giving what they play a kind of calm impact. The unique element to jazz is, of course, *swing.* It's nearly impossible to define what that is, but you know it when you hear it. Again, the best way to develop your swing feel is to try and re-create the feeling players get on recordings. Especially practice 8th notes (i.e. scales or lines) with the articulation described below.

ARTICULATION: The most common way to articulate 8th notes in jazz is to tongue the off or weak beats, which makes the line swing by giving it a more syncopated feel (pianists and guitarists create this effect by slightly accenting the same notes). Don't make the mistake of playing the off beat notes you tongue too short, as this will make your lines sound corny. *With the exception of slow tempos, every 8th note in a line is nearly the same length.* Again, it's the tonguing of off beats that makes it swing. Practice scales tonguing off beats.

ANHANG

JAZZ STYLE

Einfach gesagt, *style* ist das, was Musik zum Leben erweckt. In meiner langjährigen Zusammenarbeit mit Frank Sinatra habe ich schnell erkannt, dass es nicht nur darauf ankommt, welche Töne man spielt, sondern genau so sehr, *wie* man sie spielt. Style gibt der Musik die menschliche Qualität, die sie interessant und befriedigend macht und ist unabdingbar für überzeugenden und authentischen Jazz.

Die wesentlichen Elemente sind Tonbildung (*sound*), *time feel,* Artikulation, Phrasierung, Vibrato und Dynamik, gepaart mit einem Gespür für Musikalität. Nur indem man intensiv hervorragenden Musikern zuhört, und sich bemüht, ihren *style* nachzubilden, lassen sich diese Fertigkeiten entwickeln. Die Aufnahmen zu diesem Buch liefern etliche Beispiele dafür.

TONBILDUNG (SOUND): Als Ken Peplowski den großen Saxofonisten Sonny Stitt fragte, wie er seinen persönlichen Sound auf jedem beliebigen Saxofon erzeugt, antwortete er: "Steckt alles im Kopf." Damit meinte er, dass man eine innere Vorstellung des eigenen Sounds entwickeln muss und dazu muss man sich intensiv mit dem Spiel großer Solisten beschäftigt haben. Versuchen Sie, den Sound des Solisten innerlich zu hören, wenn Sie die Etüden üben.

TIME FEEL: Mit einer Mischung aus Entspanntheit und Intensität schaffen es die besten Musiker, jede Art von Musik spannend und eindringlich zu gestalten. Im Jazz kommt noch dieses schwer definierbare Element hinzu: *swing,* das sich eigentlich nur durch Hören und Imitieren aneignen lässt. Üben Sie dazu Skalen und Phrasen in Achteln mit der unten beschriebenen Artikulation.

ARTIKULATION: Im Jazz ist es üblich, dass Bläser die unbetonten Achtelnoten anstoßen, wodurch eine Melodielinie einen synkopierten Charakter erhält. Pianisten und Gitarristen erzielen diesen Effekt, indem sie diese Noten leicht akzentuieren. Vermeiden Sie unbedingt, die unbetonten Achtel zu kurz zu spielen. *Mit der Ausnahme sehr langsamer Tempi haben alle Achtelnoten in einer Phrase etwa dieselbe Dauer.* Noch einmal zur Betonung: der *swing* entsteht durch das Anstossen der unbetonten Achtel. Üben Sie diese Artikulation mit Tonleitern.

D MAJOR / D DUR

ANNEXES

LE STYLE JAZZ

Simplement dit, le *style* est ce qui donne vie à la musique. Durant les nombreuses années où j'ai travaillé avec Frank Sinatra, un maître styliste, j'ai rapidement réalisé que la façon de jouer les notes était au moins aussi importante que les notes elles-mêmes. Le style ajoute une qualité humaine qui rend la musique bien plus intéressante et enrichissante, et est d'une importance cruciale pour une expression convaincante et authentique en jazz.

Les éléments stylistiques essentiels du jazz sont *la sonorité, le sens de la pulsation (time feel), l'articulation, le phrasé, le vibrato et les dynamiques*, combinés avec certain sens de *la musicalité*. L'unique manière de développer ces compétences est d'écouter intensément les grands musiciens et de s'exercer à recréer leur style. L'enregistrement ci-joint vous donnera d'excellents exemples de tous ces éléments.

LA SONORITE : Lorsque Ken Peplowski demanda au grand saxophoniste Sonny Stitt comment ce dernier arrivait à produire sa sonorité personnelle depuis n'importe quel saxophone, celui-ci lui répondit: « C'est tout dans la tête ». Il voulait dire par là que l'on doit développer une représentation intérieure de sa propre sonorité, et pour cela s'être imprégné durant longtemps du jeu des grands interprètes. Lorsque vous exercez les études, essayez d'entendre dans votre tête la sonorité du soliste et recréez-la. Ecoutez particulièrement la couleur, l'équilibre et l'intensité.

LE SENS DE LA PULSATION (TIME FEEL) : Quel que soit le type de musique, les meilleurs musiciens arrivent à faire bien sonner ce qu'ils jouent. En général, cela consiste en un mélange de décontraction et d'intensité (le contraire du feeling « lazy »), ce qui fait que leur musique a de l'impact tout en restant sereine. L'élément caractéristique du jazz est bien entendu le swing. Il est pratiquement impossible de le définir, mais on le reconnaît lorsqu'on l'entend. Là aussi, le meilleur moyen de développer votre sens du swing est d'essayer et de recréer le feeling des interprètes sur leurs enregistrements. Répétez particulièrement les croches (en gammes ou en phrases) avec l'articulation indiquée ci-dessous.

L'ARTICULATION : Pour les souffleurs, la manière la plus courante d'articuler les croches en jazz est de donner un coup de langue sur la croche faible (off-beat), ce qui fait swinguer la phrase en lui conférant un effet plus syncopé. Les pianistes et guitaristes créent cet effet en accentuant légèrement les mêmes notes. Ne faites pas l'erreur de jouer les notes off-beat trop courtes : vos phrases sonneraient ringard (« corny »). *Toutes les croches d'une phrase ont pratiquement la même durée, sauf dans les tempi lents.* Encore une fois, c'est le coup de langue (l'accentuation) sur les notes faibles (off-beat) qui fait swinguer. Travaillez les gammes avec cette articulation.

RE MAJEUR

PHRASING: What I mean by phrasing is the way players use bends, grace notes and note duration (i.e. marcato, legato, staccato, etc...) to shape what they're playing. The most common mistake inexperienced players make with bends is to play them too long or too flat. Most of the time, bends are done by slightly releasing pressure of the jaw (guitarist bend the string) when attacking a note to make the pitch just a little flat, then bringing it in tune (pianist can't bend notes).

A grace note is when you actually finger the note a half step below the note you are aiming for, then quickly release up to the goal note.

Many of the note duration phrasing is indicated throughout the etudes. Pay close attention to them, being especially careful not to make shorter notes (i.e. marcato 'Λ') too short.

VIBRATO AND DYNAMICS: Vibrato is a matter of taste. Some players use very little (e.g. Miles Davis) while others may use quite a bit (e.g. Lew Tabackin). Of course, pianists cannot produce a vibrato. The important thing is to listen for this on recordings and to practice re-creating different styles of vibrato until you have mastered them. Dynamics not only apply to entire passages, but also to the tapering of a single note. Pay attention to the way players give sustained notes dynamic shading. For example, they may start a note softer, give the note a slight crescendo, then tapering off.

MUSICALITY: In the end, musicality is the overriding element that determines if something sounds good or not. The only way to develop this is by listening to players that do it, which involves instincts, judgement and a bit of undefined magic. *If you don't play musically, everything else is pretty much meaningless!*

PLAYING VARIOUS TEMPOS
Each tempo has its own set of challenges:

· Slow tempos require more variation in phrasing. Generally, more notes are articulated at slower tempos to provide more definition. It's also helpful to sometimes hear double time or a 6/8 tempo while playing slower tempos, as it can help „energize" the time and keep it from slowing down further.

· Medium tempos are often about consistency of time (e.g. groove) and phrasing. Many inexperienced players articulate either too much or too many downbeats, making the line feel choppy or heavy. Eighth note lines are generally played with upbeat (or weakbeat) articulation, helping the line to both flow and swing.

· Fast tempos generally require less variation in phrasing. In fact, at extreme tempos, there's actually very little articulation. Clean technique is a critical factor with fast tempos, allowing lines to sound clear without the help of articulation. Hearing the tempo in half time can bring a sense of calm and relaxation to fast tempos. For example, if the tempo is ♩= 160, hear the time as 𝅝=80.

PHRASIERUNG: Unter Phrasierung verstehe ich die Gestaltung mit *bends,* Vorschlägen (*grace notes*) und Dauern (legato, marcato, staccato, etc.) Unerfahrene Bläser machen häufig den Fehler, einen *bend* zu lang zu spielen oder zu tief anzusetzen. Es reicht, beim Ansatz den Kieferdruck etwas zu lockern und dann die Note auf die richtige Tonhöhe zu ziehen. Gitarristen dehnen und entspannen die Saite – Pianisten haben das Nachsehen.

Ein Vorschlag wird gewöhnlich einen Halbton unter dem Zielton gegriffen und dann schnell aufgelöst.

Phrasierungs- und Artikulationsanweisungen finden sich in jeder Etüde. Achten Sie besonders darauf, kurze Noten (marcato, 'Λ') nicht zu kurz zu spielen.

VIBRATO UND DYNAMIK: Vibrato ist Geschmackssache. Manche Spieler benutzen sehr wenig (z.B. Miles Davis), andere umso mehr (z.B. Lew Tabackin). Hören Sie sich verschiedene Vibratostile an und versuchen Sie sie zu reproduzieren, bis Sie sie beherrschen. Dynamik bezieht sich nicht nur auf gesamte Passagen sondern auch auf die Gestaltung einer einzelnen Note, besonders wenn sie gehalten wird. Sie können z.B. eine Note leise beginnen, ein leichtes Crescendo anbringen und wieder leise ausklingen lassen.

MUSIKALITÄT: Letztlich entscheidet aber ein gutes musikalisches Gespür über die Qualität einer Darbietung. Diese Musikalität lässt sich nur durch intensives Zuhören erwerben und entwickeln, mit Instinkt, Urteilsvermögen und diesem schwer definierbaren Quentchen Magie. Ohne das ist alles andere ziemlich bedeutungslos.

IN VERSCHIEDENEN TEMPI SPIELEN
Jedes Tempo hat seine eigenen Herausforderungen:

· Langsame Tempi erfordern eine abwechslungsreichere Phrasierung. In langsameren Tempi werden meist mehr Noten artikuliert, um dem Stück mehr Klarheit zu verleihen. Außerdem ist es hilfreich, ein langsames Stück beim Spielen hin und wieder im doppelten Tempo bzw. 6/8-Takt zu hören, da es dadurch spannender und wird und man verhindert, noch langsamer zu werden.

· Bei mittelschnellen Tempi geht es oft darum, dass Takt (z. B. der Groove) und Phrasierung eingehalten werden. Viele unerfahrene Musiker artikulieren entweder insgesamt zu viel oder betonen die Eins zu oft. Dadurch klingt das Stück dann oft abgehackt und schwer. Achtelpassagen werden generell mit schwacher Betonung (synkopisch) gespielt, damit sie flüssig klingen und swingen.

· Schnelle Tempi erfordern im Allgemeinen weniger Abwechslung bei der Phrasierung. Bei extrem schnellen Tempi muss sogar nur noch sehr wenig artikuliert werden. Eine gute Technik ist bei schnellen Tempi sehr wichtig, damit alle Noten auch ohne das Hilfsmittel der Artikulation deutlich zu hören sind. Wenn man das Stück beim Spielen im halben Tempo hört, kann man etwas Ruhe und Entspannung in schnelle Tempi bringen. Wenn das Tempo z. B. ♩ = 160 ist, hört man es als 𝅝 = 80.

LE PHRASE : Ce que j'appelle phrasé est la façon dont les interprètes utilisent le portamento (notes portées/bend notes), les appoggiatures (grace notes) ainsi que les durées des notes (c.à.d. marcato, legato, staccato, etc.), afin de « modeler » ce qu'ils jouent. L'erreur la plus courante que les souffleurs inexpérimentés font avec les bend notes est de les tenir trop longtemps ou de les jouer trop bas. La plupart du temps, on exécute les bend notes en relâchant légèrement la pression de la mâchoire à l'attaque de la note, de façon à la jouer juste un peu trop bas, puis à la « porter » jusqu'à sa hauteur correcte. Les guitaristes tendent puis relâchent la corde – les pianistes ne peuvent pas jouer de bend notes.

Une appoggiature est souvent jouée un demi-ton en dessous de la note-cible, et relâchée rapidement.

De nombreuses indications de phrasé sont indiquées dans toutes les études. Soyez-y très attentif, en veillant particulièrement à ne pas jouer les notes courtes (marcato, 'Λ') trop courtes.

LE VIBRATO ET LES DYNAMIQUES : Le vibrato est une question de goût. Certains interprètes, comme Miles Davis, ne l'utilisent que peu, tandis que d'autres, comme Lew Tabackin, en usent plus généreusement. Bien entendu, les pianistes ne peuvent pas produire de vibrato. L'important est d'y prêter attention en écoutant les enregistrements, et de vous exercer à reproduire différents styles de vibrato jusqu'à ce que vous les ayez maîtrisés.

Les dynamiques ne s'appliquent pas uniquement à des passages entiers, mais également à l'émission d'une seule note. Soyez attentifs à la façon qu'ont les interprètes de donner aux notes tenues des nuances dynamiques. Ils peuvent par exemple commencer par jouer une note doucement, faire un léger crescendo, puis diminuer graduellement.

LA MUSICALITE : Pour terminer, la musicalité est l'élément prépondérant qui détermine la qualité d'une exécution. La seule façon de l'acquérir et de la développer est d'écouter les interprètes qui en font preuve ; elle implique de l'instinct, de la capacité de jugement et un zeste de magie indéfinissable. *Si vous ne jouez pas avec musicalité, tout le reste est pratiquement dénué de sens !*

JOUER DANS DIFFÉRENTS TEMPI

Chaque tempo présente sa propre série d'exigences :

· Les tempi lents requièrent un phrasé plus varié. De manière générale, dans les tempi lents, on articule un plus grand nombre de notes afin de mieux caractériser l'ensemble de la phrase. On peut aussi s'aider parfois, lorsqu'on joue des tempi lents, en entendant la pièce au double du tempo, ou en 6/8, car cela peut donner de l'énergie au jeu, tout en évitant de ralentir.

· Les tempi medium sont souvent dépendants de la cohérence des temps (cf. le groove), comme du phrasé. De nombreux musiciens inexpérimentés accentuent trop ou trop souvent les temps faibles, ce qui rend la ligne instable ou pesante. Les phrasés de croches se jouent généralement en upbeat (ou en temps faibles), ce qui aide à la fluidité comme au swing de la ligne.

· Les tempi rapides requièrent généralement moins de variations de phrasé. En fait, dans les tempi extrêmement rapides, il n'est besoin que de très peu d'articulation. La précision technique est un facteur essentiel dans les tempi rapides, en permettant aux lignes de sonner en toute clarté sans besoin d'articuler. Entendre le tempo à la blanche peut procurer une sensation de calme et de détente dans les tempi rapides. Par exemple, si le tempo est de 160 à la blanche, entendez-le comme s'il s'agissait de 80 à la ronde.

SCALES WITH CORRELATING LINES

Here are many of the scales that are the theoretical basis for creating lines throughout this book. The chord symbol is given along with the essential notes that define the chord's sound, as well as the related scale and a line extracted from one of the etudes. *The chord/scale examples have all been transposed to C, the melodic ideas to B♭ concert.*

Always keep in mind that it's extremely important to see how the lines are used within the context of the piece. For example, many of these scales are modes of other scales (i.e. Mixolydian is the 5th mode of major, Spanish is the 5th mode of harmonic minor) and really are used in a melodic way related to the key they belong to. In other words, they are usually within a chord progression that melodically comes from and leads to something.

SKALEN UND ZUGEHÖRIGE PHRASENBEISPIELE

Viele der Skalen, die den theoretischen Hintergrund für die Phrasen in diesem Buch bilden, werden hier vorgestellt. Zu jeder wird das Akkordsymbol gezeigt, die wesentlichen Akkordtöne, die Skala selbst und ein Beispiel aus einer der Etüden in diesem Buch. *Die Akkord-/Skalenbeispiele sind in C notiert, die melodischen Beispiele in klingend B♭.*

Es ist sehr wichtig, die Phrasen im Kontext des jeweiligen Stückes zu betrachten. Viele der Skalen sind Modi anderer Tonleitern (z.B. ist Mixolydisch der fünfte Modus in Dur, die "spanische Skala" ist der fünfte Modus von harmonisch Moll). Melodisch stehen sie aber im Bezug zur jeweiligen Tonart und Akkordfolge. Anders ausgedrückt: sie sind Teil einer melodisch/harmonischen Entwicklung, die aus etwas entsteht und woanders hinführt.

AUTUMN, MS. 33–36

The notes on Am⁷ create the D dominant bebop scale. But the melodic content of the entire line puts the scale in a musical context of G major.

Unter dem Am⁷ Akkord bilden die Melodietöne die mixolydische Tonleiter auf D. Der harmonische Kontext der gesamten Phrase ist allerdings G Dur.

All chord/scale examples are transposed to C.

"Δ" indicates major 7
"–" indicates minor.

Alle Akkord-/Skalenbeispiele sind nach C transponiert.

"Δ" bedeutet "major 7" (große Septime)
"–" bedeutet "Moll".

GAMMES AVEC PHRASES CORRESPONDANTES

Voici quelques-unes des gammes formant dans ce livre la base théorique servant à créer des phrases. Pour chacune d'entre elles, le symbole d'accord est noté, tout comme les notes essentielles de l'accord, la gamme elle-même, ainsi qu'un exemple tiré d'une des études de ce livre. *Les examples de gammes avec phrases correspondantes sont transposées en C, les examples mélodiques pour l'improvisation sont transposés en B♭.*

Rappelez-vous toujours qu'il est extrêmement important de considérer les phrases dans le contexte de la pièce. Par exemple, plusieurs de ces gammes sont des modes d'autres gammes (le mode mixolydien, p.ex., est le cinquième mode de la gamme majeure, et la « gamme espagnole » est le cinquième mode de la gamme harmonique mineure). Cependant, elles sont utilisées mélodiquement parlant en relation avec leur tonalité ou suite d'accords respectives. Autrement dit, elles font en général partie d'une suite d'accords qui, mélodiquement, vient de quelque part et conduit quelque part.

AUTUMN, MES. 33-36

Les notes de Am⁷ forment la gamme mixolydienne de D. Mais le contenu mélodique de la phrase entière inscrit la gamme dans le contexte harmonique de G majeur.

Toutes les gammes avec phrases correspondantes sont transposées en C.

« Δ » signifie « major 7 » (7e majeure),
« – » signifie mineur.

EXTRACTED LINES AND MELODIC IDEAS FOR IMPROVISATION

Learning lines and melodic ideas over a variety of chords and keys will help give you the vocabulary you need to begin to create meaningful solos. Some lines lay better in one key than another, some ideas (usually within a small range), work well in many keys.

Though the lines have been transposed to B♭ concert, try to learn at least some of them in every key. This will greatly increase your ability to improvise through more complex changes, build technique, and help you to visualize key centers.

If you like a particular line and want to use it when soloing, you obviously must commit it to memory. When memorizing a line, most people think of the notes as positions on the chord or scale. At the same time, try to anticipate the sound of the line with your ears. The idea is to become completely comfortable with the line so you can play it on demand.

MELODISCHE BEISPIELE UND IDEEN FÜR DIE IMPROVISATION

Melodische Phrasen über eine Vielzahl von Akkorden in verschiedenen Tonarten zu lernen, wird Ihnen helfen, ein Vokabular für aussagekräftige Solos aufzubauen. Nicht alle liegen gleich gut in allen Tonarten, aber manche (mit geringerem Umfang) lassen sich leicht transponieren.

Die Beispiele sind zwar alle nach klingend B♭ transponiert, versuchen Sie aber trotzdem wenigstens einige in allen Tonarten zu lernen. So verbessern Sie Ihre Fähigkeit über komplexere Akkordfolgen zu improvisieren, tonale Zentren zu visualisieren und Ihre Technik.

Um eine Phrase, die Ihnen gefällt, auch im Solospiel einzusetzen, müssen Sie sie zwangsläufig in Erinnerung behalten. Die meisten Musiker merken sich Melodietöne anhand ihrer Position im Akkord oder der Tonleiter. Versuchen Sie gleichzeitig, die Melodie innerlich vorweg zu hören, so dass Sie sie jederzeit abrufen können.

TOTAL BLUES, MS. 37-40

After memorizing some of these lines, go back to the etude and see how they are used within context. Timing (the way lines and ideas are linked together) and pacing (the way the solo unfolds) are completely critical, creating a certain flow and allowing the ideas to compliment each other. Without studying context, your solos will sound very mechanical.

Haben Sie einige dieser Phrasen auswendig gelernt, betrachten Sie sie nochmals im Kontext der jeweiligen Etüde. Wichtig ist, wie die Phrasen verbunden sind (*timing*) und wie sie sich im Verlauf der Etüde entwickeln (*pacing*), so dass ein fliessender Eindruck entsteht, bei dem die Ideen einander ergänzen. Ohne den Kontext zu beachten, werden Ihre Solos sehr mechanisch klingen.

EXEMPLES MELODIQUES ET IDEES POUR L'IMPROVISATION

Apprenez des phrases et des idées mélodiques sur une grande variété d'accords et dans différentes tonalités : cela vous aidera à développer le vocabulaire dont vous avez besoin pour créer des solos cohérents. Certaines phrases sonneront mieux dans une tonalité plutôt que dans une autre, mais certaines idées (de préférence sur une amplitude réduite) se laisseront facilement transposer.

Bien que les phrases aient été transposées en B♭, essayez d'en apprendre au moins quelques-unes dans toutes les tonalités. Ceci va énormément améliorer votre capacité à improviser sur des suites d'accords plus complexes, renforcer votre technique et vous aider à visualiser les centres tonaux.

Si vous souhaitez insérer dans vos solos une phrase qui vous plaît, vous devez évidemment la mémoriser. Pour ce faire, la majorité des musiciens retiennent les notes d'après leur position dans l'accord ou la gamme. Simultanément, essayez d'entendre à l'avance, en vous, la mélodie de la phrase. Le but est de vous sentir parfaitement à l'aise avec cette phrase, de façon à pouvoir la rejouer en tout temps.

TOTAL BLUES, MES. 37-40

Après avoir mémorisé certaines de ces phrases, reprenez l'étude et observez dans quel contexte elles sont employées. Le timing (la façon dont les phrases et idées sont liées entre elles) et le pacing (la façon dont le solo se développe) sont essentiels : ensemble, ils créent une impression de flux et permettent aux idées de se compléter les unes les autres. Sans une étude du contexte, vos solos sonneront très mécaniques.

EXTRACTED LINES (TRANSPOSED TO B♭)

MAJOR 2-MEASURE II-V'S RESOLVING TO I (A–7 D7 G∆)

EXAMPLES MÉLODIQUES (TRANSPOSÉS EN B♭)

II-V-I MAJEURE SUR QUATRE MESURES (A–7 D7 G∆)

PHRASENBEISPIELE (IN KLINGEND B♭)

VIERTAKTIGE II-V-I VERBINDUNGEN IN DUR (A–7 D7 G∆)

MINOR 2-MEASURE II-V'S RESOLVING TO I
(A∅ D7 G–)

II-V-I MINEURE SUR QUATRE MESURES
(A∅ D7 G–)

VIERTAKTIGE II-V-I VERBINDUNGEN IN MOLL
(A∅ D7 G–)

MAJOR 1-MEASURE II-V OR V RESOLVING TO I
(A–7 D7 GΔ, unless otherwise indicated)

II-V-I MAJEURE SUR DEUX MESURES
(sauf indication contraire, A-7 D7 GΔ)

ZWEITAKTIGE II-V-I VERBINDUNGEN IN DUR
(A–7 D7 GΔ, wenn nicht anders angegeben)

MINOR 1-MEASURE II-V OR V RESOLVING TO I
(AØ D7♭9 G–, unless otherwise indicated)

II-V-I MINEURE SUR DEUX MESURES
(sauf indication contraire, AØ D7 G–)

ZWEITAKTIGE II-V-I VERBINDUNGEN IN MOLL
(AØ D7♭9 G–, wenn nicht anders angegeben)

SOME BLUES IDEAS   **EXAMPLES BLUES**   **EINIGE BLUES BEISPIELE**

TURNAROUNDS: B-7 E7 A-7 D7

unless otherwise indicated   sauf indication contraire   wenn nicht anders angegeben

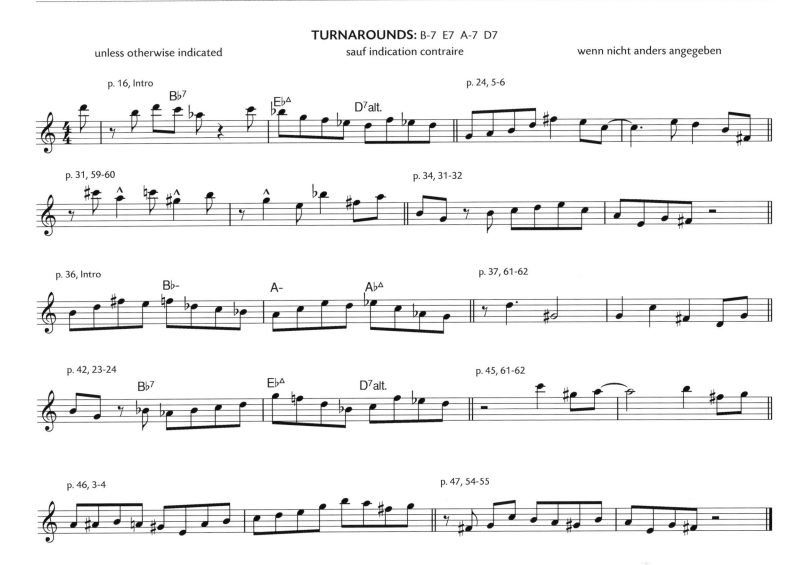

CREATING VOCABULARY STUDIES

Over the years, I have known many master musicians that have created vocabulary studies of specific ideas (e.g. "licks") they are learning, then often transposing the studies to every key. There are several benefits to this method:

· Puts groups of ideas in context over a common chord progression in a single key
· Speeds up integration of ideas into your playing
· Helps to develop timing, pacing and balance over longer sections (8, 16, 32 ms)
· Develops technical flow and appropriate phrasing
· When transposed, builds logical vocabulary and familiarity with difficult keys

Try picking out ideas that you like from the etudes and creating your own vocabulary studies. It could be over one chord (e. g. mi7, V7, maj7), II-V-I in either major or minor, III-VI-II-V, and so on.

Here are two 16-measure examples based on two of the most common chord progressions in jazz: II-V-I in both major and minor. The ideas have been extracted from various etudes and transposed to C concert.

ÜBUNG ZUM AUFBAU EINES MELODISCHEN VOKABULARS

Im Laufe der Jahre habe ich viele großartige Musiker kennengelernt, die Phrasen aus bestimmten melodischen Ideen (sog. "Licks") entwickelt haben, die sie dann in alle Tonarten transponiert haben. Diese Methode hat mehrere Vorteile:

· Sie stellt mehrere Ideen über eine gängige Akkordverbindung in einen Zusammenhang.
· Sie hilft Ihnen, diese Ideen in Ihr Spiel zu integrieren.
· Sie hilft Ihnen, Ihr Timing, eine sinnvolle Platzierung der Phrasen und eine Balance über einen längeren Abschnitt zu entwickeln (8, 16, 32 Takte).
· Sie verbessert die Geläufigkeit und Phrasierung.
· Sie hilft Ihnen beim Aufbau eines sinnvollen Vokabulars und führt zu mehr Sicherheit in schwierigen Tonarten.

Suchen Sie Phrasen in den Etüden, die Ihnen gefallen, und entwickeln Sie eigene Übungen daraus. Sie können über einen Akkord gespielt werden (z.B. mi7, V7, maj7), eine II-V-I-Verbindung in Dur oder Moll, eine III-VI-II-V-Verbindung usw.

Hier sind zwei 16-taktige Beispiele über die bekanntesten Akkordverbindungen im Jazz, eine II-V-I-Verbindung in Dur bzw. Moll. Die Phrasen darin stammen von verschiedenen Etüden und sind nach klingend C transponiert.

Exercise in Major

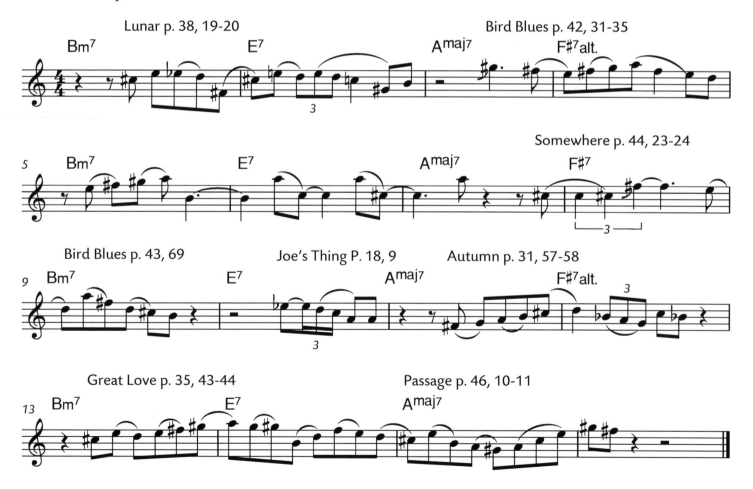

ÉTUDES DE VOCABULAIRE

Au fil des ans, j'ai rencontré un grand nombre de grands musiciens qui ont été amenés à créer des études de vocabulaire consacrés à des idées spécifiques (comme les « licks ») dont ils se servent dans leur enseignement, souvent en les faisant transposer dans tous les tons. De manière fort positive, cette pratique permet notamment :

· de regrouper des idées dans un contexte harmonique commun (enchaînements d'accords dans une seule tonalité) ;
· d'augmenter la vitesse d'assimilation des idées dans le jeu ;
· d'aider à développer le sens du timing, du phrasé et de l'équilibre dans le cadre de sections plus longues (8, 16 et 32 mesures) ;
· d'améliorer la fluidité technique et le phrasé ;
· par leur transposition, d'élaborer un vocabulaire logique, et de se familiariser avec les tonalités difficiles.

Essayez de vous approprier les idées qui vous plaisent dans ces études, et de vous en servir pour créer vos propres études de vocabulaire. Vous pouvez le faire sur un accord (par ex., mi7, V7, maj7), II-V-I, en majeur ou en mineur, III-VI-II-V, etc.

Voici un exemple de 16 mesures basé sur deux enchaînements d'accords parmi les plus fréquents du jazz : II-V-I, mineur et majeur. Ces processus ont été tirés de différentes études et transposées sur do.

Exercise in Minor

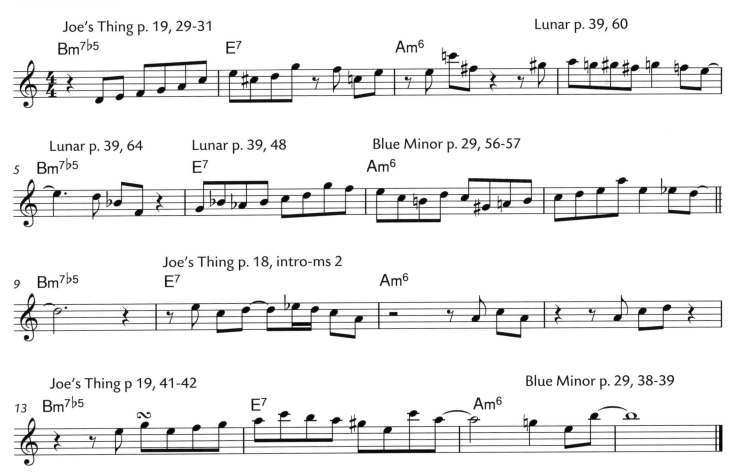

- 65 -

SUGGESTED LISTENING / HÖREMPFEHLUNGEN / L'ÉCOUTE

These recordings influenced the etudes in this book and are essential listening for any student of jazz.

Die folgenden Aufnahmen beeinflussten die Etüden in diesem Buch und sind eine unverzichtbare Hörempfehlung für jeden Jazzmusiker.

Ces enregistrements ont influencé les etudes dans ce livre et sont à l'écoute indispensable pour tout étudiant de jazz.

Groove Blues (Blues in F concert)
Charlie Parker: *Now's the Time*, Now's the Time (Verve)
Miles Davis: *Walkin'*, Walkin'(Prestige)
Miles Davis: *Straight, No Chaser*, Milestone (Columbia)

Amen
Horace Silver: *The Preacher*, Horace Silver and the Jazz Messengers (Blue Note)

A Doll
Duke Ellington: *Satin Doll*, various recordings
Red Garland: *Satin Doll*, Satin Doll (Prestige)

Total Blues
Miles Davis: *All Blues*, Kind of Blue (Columbia)
Miles Davis: *All Blues*, My Funny Valentine (Columbia)

Grease (B♭ Blues)
Charlie Parker: *Parker's Mood* (various labels)

Rose
Louis Armstrong: *Honeysuckle Rose* (various labels)
Thelonious Monk: *Honeysuckle Rose*,
The Unique Thelonious Monk (Riverside)

Joe's Thing (F minor blues)
Joe Henderson: *Out of the Night*, Page One (Blue Note)
Dizzy Gillespie: *Birk's Works*, various recordings

Proxy
Miles Davis: *Doxy*, Bags Groove (Prestige)

Father Song
Horace Silver: *Song for My Father*, Song for My Father (Blue Note)

IND Line
Duke Ellington: *Take the A Train* (various labels)
Joe Henderson: *Take the A Train*, Lush Life (Verve)

Miles
Miles Davis: *So What*, Kind of Blue (Columbia)

Blue Minor (C minor blues)
John Coltrane: *Mr. PC*, Giant Steps (Atlantic)

Autumn
Cannonball Adderley: *Autumn Leaves*, Somethin' Else (Blue Note)
Miles Davis: *Autumn Leaves*, Miles Davis in Europe (Columbia)

Friends
Charlie Parker: *Just Friends*, Bird with Strings (Verve)
Sonny Stitt: *Just Friends*, Tune Up (Muse)

Great Love
Miles Davis: *There Is No Greater Love*, Miles (Prestige)
Gene Ammons/Sonny Stitt: *There Is No Greater Love*, Boss Tenors (Verve)

Two Plus Two
Miles Davis: *Four*, Blue Haze (Prestige)
Miles Davis: *"Four"* and More (Columbia)

Lunar
Miles Davis: *Solar*, Walkin' (Prestige)

Tunisia
Charlie Parker: *A Night in Tunisia* (various labels)
Art Blakey: *A Night in Tunisia*, A Night in Tunisia (Blue Note)

Bird Blues
Charlie Parker: *Cool Blues*, (various labels)

Somewhere
Charlie Parker: *Out Of Nowhere* (various labels)

Passage
Miles Davis: *Oleo*, Bags Groove (Prestige)
Miles Davis: *Oleo*, Relaxin' (Prestige)
Charlie Parker: *Anthropology* (various labels)

BIOGRAPHIES

Jim Snidero is considered to be one of the top alto saxophonists in jazz. A New York resident since 1981, he has been voted into *Downbeat* Magazine's Readers Poll, and one of his albums was included in *The Penguin Jazz Guide: The History of the Music in the 1001 Best Albums*. As a leader, he has over 18 recordings for EMI, Milestone, Savant, Criss-Cross and Red among others, and has been a member of many distinguished groups, including The Mingus Big Band, Brother Jack McDuff, Eddie Palmieri, Maria Schneider, Toshiko Akiyoshi, Frank Wess,and Frank Sinatra, among others.
Snidero is an adjunct professor at New School University, and was a visiting professor at both Indiana University and Princeton University. He is the founder of The Jazz Conception Company, www.jazzimprovisation.com.
Visit Jim Snidero on the internet at www.jimsnidero.com

Mike LeDonne has performed and recorded with some of the greatest jazz artists of all time, including Dizzy Gillespie, Sonny Rollins, Milt Jackson, Benny Golson and Bobby Hutcherson, among many. Equally talented on both the piano and B-3 organ, LeDonne was voted into *Downbeat* Magazine's Critics Poll, has over 15 recordings as a leader and appears on over 40 recording as a sideman. LeDonne performs frequently in New York, and tours internationally with his own groups and others, and has an active private teaching studio.

Dennis Irwin (1951-2008) was a member of one of the most important groups in jazz history, *Art Blakey and The Jazz Messengers*, appearing on nine Jazz Messenger recordings. Irwin was also a member of groups led by Horace Silver, Stan Getz, Chet Baker, Johnny Griffin, Joe Lovano, John Scofield, Tania Maria and Mel Lewis, among others. He is greatly missed by the jazz community.

Kenny Washington is one of the most recorded drummers in jazz history, appearing many times in *Downbeat* Magazine's Critics Poll. Since the early 1980's, Washington has appeared on countless recordings and been a member of many distinguished groups led by Dizzy Gillespie, Sonny Stitt, Lee Konitz, Tommy Flanagan, Cedar Walton, Ahmad Jamal, Phil Woods, Lionel Hampton, Johnny Griffin, Clark Terry and Betty Carter, among others.

© Jim Snidero

BIOGRAFIEN

Jim Snidero gilt als einer der besten Altsaxophonisten im Jazz. Der seit 1981 in New York lebende Musiker erhielt eine Platzierung im Readers Poll der Zeitschrift *Downbeat,* und eins seiner Alben wurde in den *Penguin Jazz Guide: The History of the Music in the 1001 Best Albums* aufgenommen. Als Bandleader nahm er 18 Alben auf, u. a. für die Labels EMI, Milestone, Savant, Criss Cross und Red. Darüber hinaus war er Mitglied zahlreicher bekannter Gruppen, u. a. The Mingus Big Band, Brother Jack McDuff, Eddie Palmieri, Maria Schneider, Toshiko Akiyoshi, Frank Wess und Frank Sinatra.
Snidero ist Assistenzprofessor an der New School University und war Gastprofessor sowohl an der Indiana University als auch an der Princeton University. Er ist Gründer der Jazz Conception Company: www.jazzimprovisation.com.
Besuchen Sie Jim Snidero im Internet: www.jimsnidero.com

Mike LeDonne hat mit einigen der berühmtesten Jazzmusikern aller Zeiten zusammengearbeitet, z. B. Dizzy Gillespie, Sonny Rollins, Milt Jackson, Benny Golson, Bobby Hutcherson und vielen anderen. LeDonne, der sowohl auf dem Klavier als auch auf der Hammond B3 brilliert, platzierte sich im Critics Poll der Zeitschrift *Downbeat,* hat über 15 Alben als Bandleader aufgenommen und ist auf über 40 Aufnahmen als Sideman zu hören. LeDonne tritt häufig in New York auf, tourt weltweit mit seinen eigenen und anderen Gruppen und hat ein eigenes Unterrichtsstudio.

Dennis Irwin (1951-2008) war Mitglied einer der bekanntesten Gruppen der Jazzgeschichte, *Art Blakey and The Jazz Messengers,* und ist auf neun Jazz-Messenger-Aufnahmen zu hören. Darüber hinaus war Irwin Mitglied in Bands, die u.a. von Horace Silver, Stan Getz, Chet Baker, Johnny Griffin, Joe Lovano, John Scofield, Tania Maria, Mel Lewis geleitet wurden. Sein Tod ist ein schmerzlicher Verlust für die gesamte Jazz Community.

Kenny Washington gehört zu den Drummerm mit den meisten Aufnahmen der Jazzgeschichte und platzierte sich mehrmals im Critics Poll der Zeitschrift *Downbeat.* Seit Anfang der 1980er-Jahre ist Washington auf zahllosen Aufnahmen zu hören und war Mitglied vieler bekannter Gruppen, u. a. von Dizzy Gillespie, Sonny Stitt, Lee Konitz, Tommy Flanagan, Cedar Walton, Ahmad Jamal, Phil Woods, Lionel Hampton, Johnny Griffin, Clark Terry und Betty Carter.

BIOGRAPHIES

Jim Snidero est considéré comme un des saxophonistes alto de tout premier plan dans le jazz. Résidant à New York depuis 1981, il a été élu par le sondage des lecteurs du magazine *Downbeat* , et un de ses albums est cité dans le *Guide Penguin du Jazz: l'histoire de la musique par ses 1001 meilleurs albums.* En tant que leader, il a notamment effectué plus de 18 enregistrements pour EMI, Milestone, Savant, Criss Cross et Red; il été membre de nombreux groupes célèbres et joué avec des artistes connus, parmi lesquels The Mingus Big Band, Brother Jack McDuff, Eddie Palmieri, Maria Schneider, Toshiko Akiyoshi, Frank Wess, et Frank Sinatra.
Snidero est professeur associé à la New School University de New York, et professeur invité aux universités d'Indiana et de Princeton. Il est le fondateur de la Jazz Conception Company, www.jazzimprovisation.com
Allez sur son site: www.jimsnidero. com

Mike LeDonne a joué et enregistré avec certains des plus grands artistes de jazz de tous les temps comme Dizzie Gillespie, Sonny Rollins, Milt Jackson, Benny Golson et Bobby Hutcherson, parmi tant d'autres. Talentueux aussi bien au piano qu'à l'orgue Hammond B-3, LeDonne a été élu par la commission des critiques du magazine *Downbeat*; il a été leader de plus de 15 enregistrements, et a collaboré à plus de quarante autres. LeDonne joue fréquemment à New York, et effectue des tournées internationales avec ses propres groupes ou d'autres partenaires; il est à la tête d'un studio privé d'enseignement.

Dennis Irwin (1951-2008) a fait partie de l'un des groupes les plus importants de l'histoire du jazz, *Art Blakey et les Jazz Messengers,* connus par ses neuf disques signés Jazz Messengers. Irwin a également fait partie des formations de Horace Silver, Stan Getz, Chet Baker, Johnny Griffin, Joe Lovano, John Scofield, Tania Maria et Mel Lewis, entre autres. Il manque cruellement à la communauté du jazz.

Kenny Washington est l'un des batteurs les plus enregistrés de l'histoire du jazz, et fréquemment mentionné dans le cadre de la commission des critiques du magazine *Downbeat.* Depuis le début des années 1980, Washington a participé à d'innombrables enregistrements, et fait partie des groupes les plus en vue, conduits par Dizzy Gillespie, Sonny Stitt, Lee Konitz, Tommy Flanagan, Cedar Walton, Ahmad Jamal, Phil Woods, Lionel Hampton, Johnny Griffin, Clark Terry et Betty Carter, pour ne citer qu'eux.